Guitar Tablature Vocal.

Published 2002
© International Music Publications Ltd
Griffin House 161 Hammersmith Road London W6 8BS England

Edited by Chris Harvey.
Music arranged by Artemis Music Ltd.
Design and art direction by Mat Maitland at Big Active.
Illustration by David Foldvari.
Hi-Fi Serious logo by Daniel P. Carter.
Folio design by Dominic Brookman.

Reproducing this music in any form is illegal and forbidden by the Copyright, Designs and Patents Act, 1988

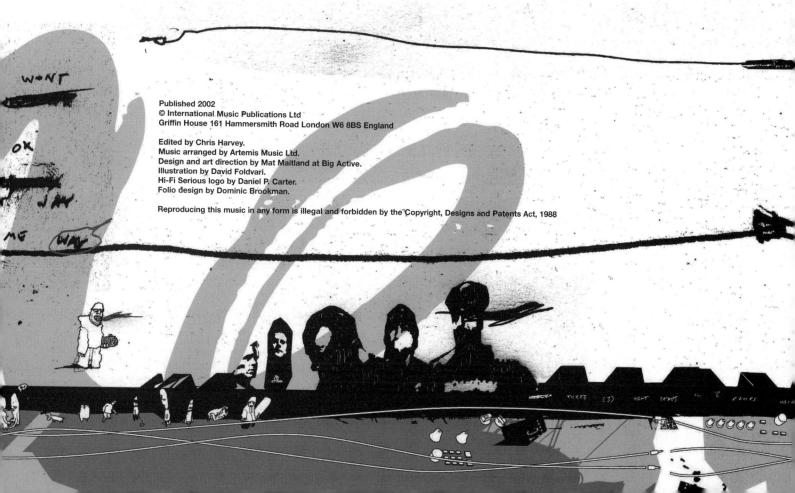

# Nothing.

**Words and Music by Adam Perry, Giles Perry,
Mark Chapman, Daniel Carter and Jason Perry**

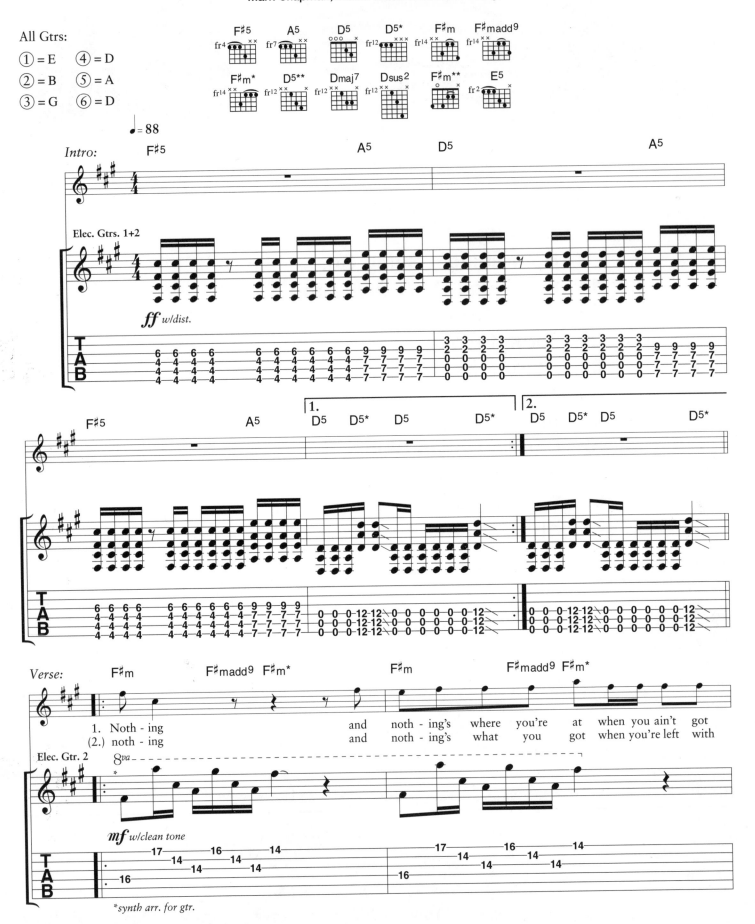

*synth arr. for gtr.

© 2001 Warner/Chappell Music Publishing Ltd, London W6 8BS

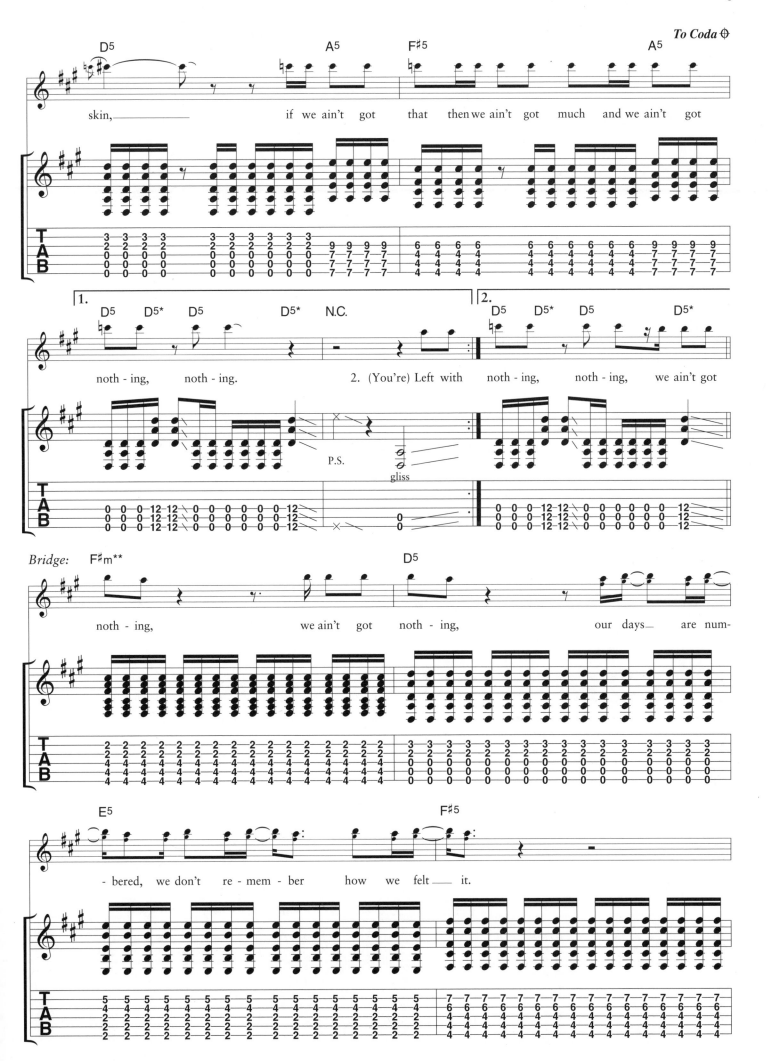

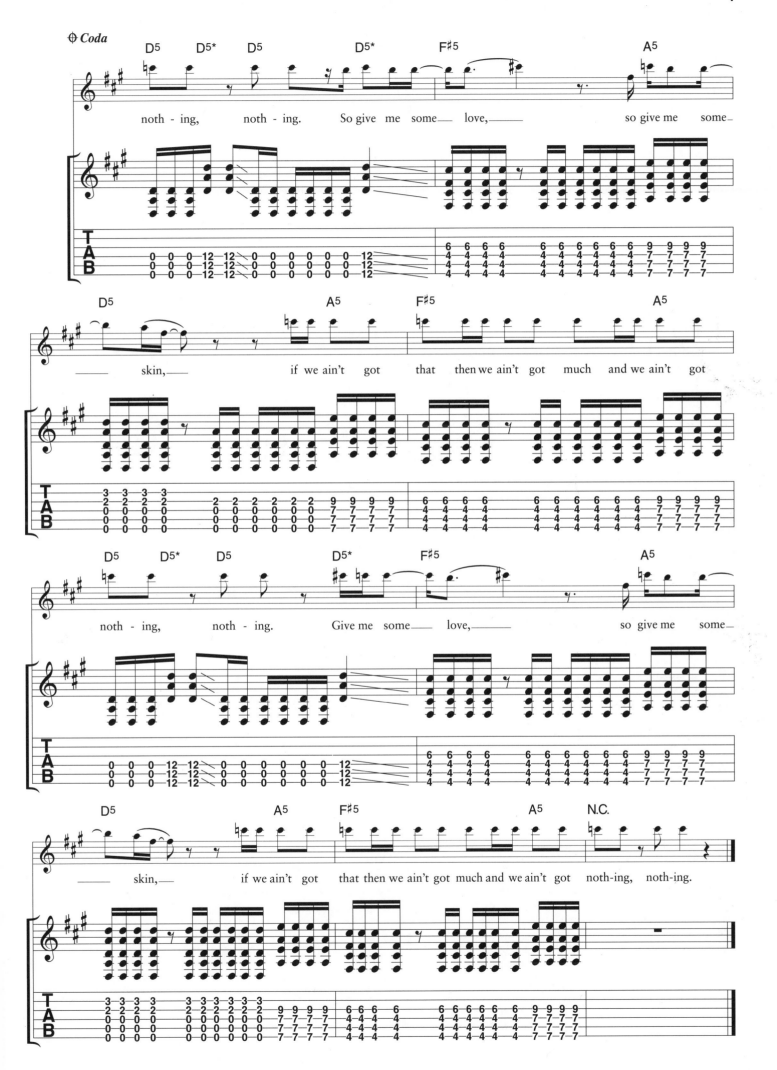

# Something's Going On.

Words and Music by Adam Perry, Giles Perry,
Mark Chapman, Daniel Carter and Jason Perry

© 2001 Warner/Chappell Music Publishing Ltd, London W6 8BS

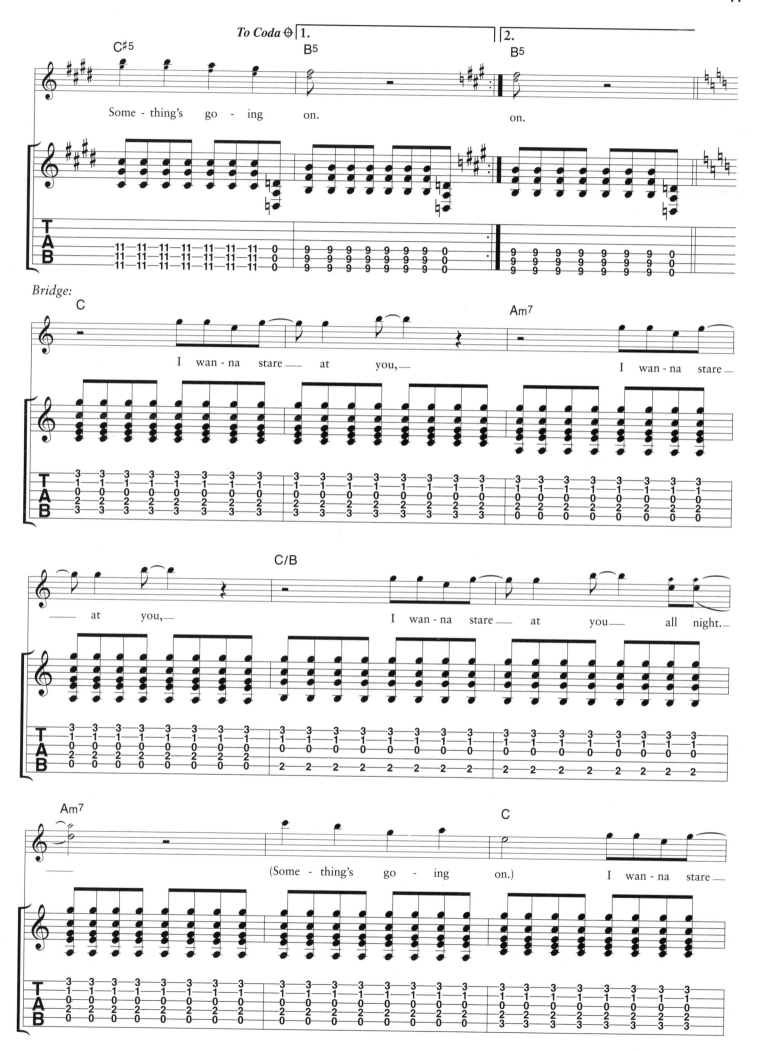

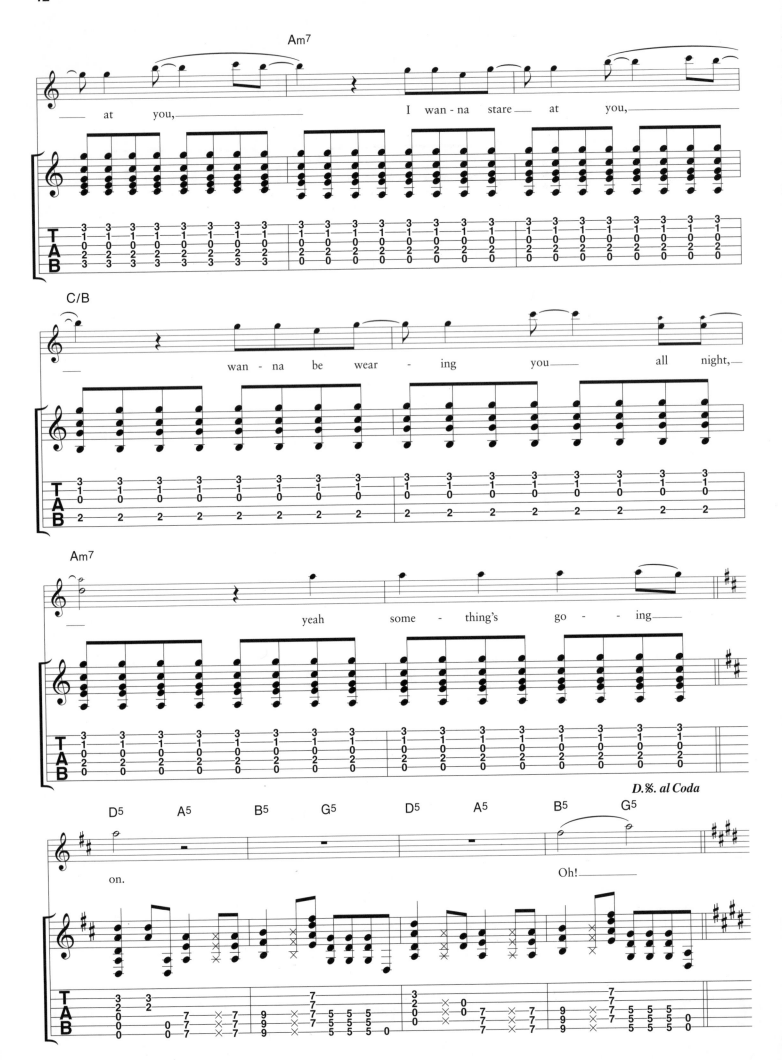

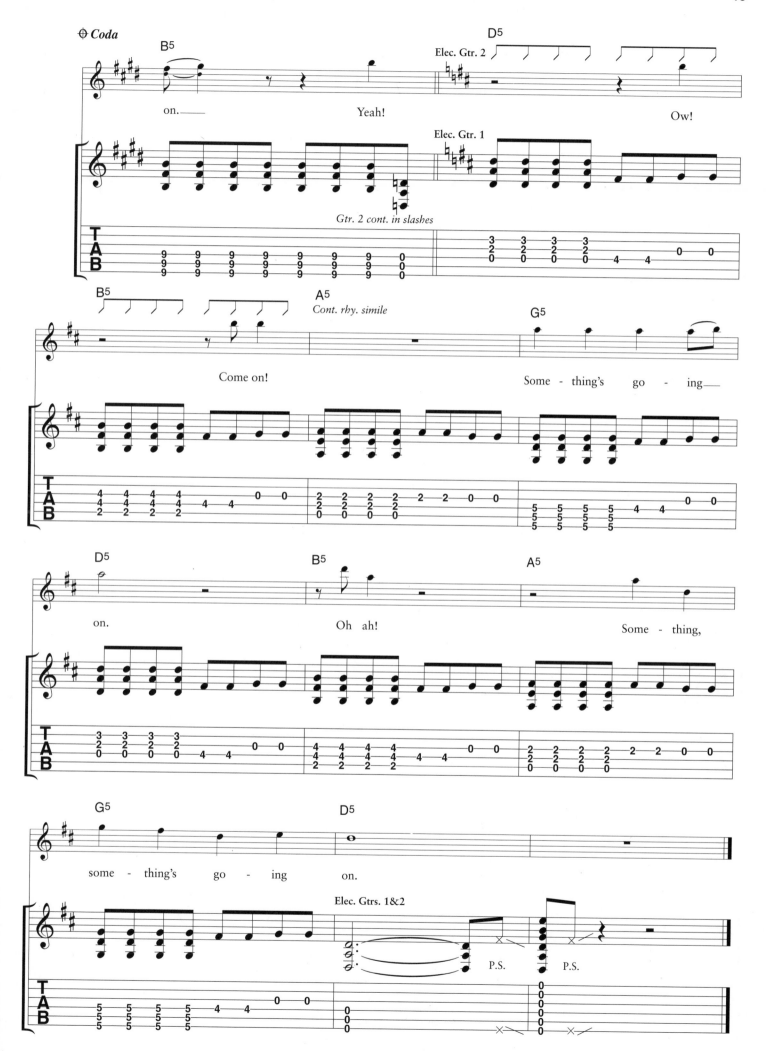

# Six O'clock On A Tube Stop.

Words and Music by Adam Perry, Giles Perry,
Mark Chapman, Daniel Carter and Jason Perry

© 2001 Warner/Chappell Music Publishing Ltd, London W6 8BS

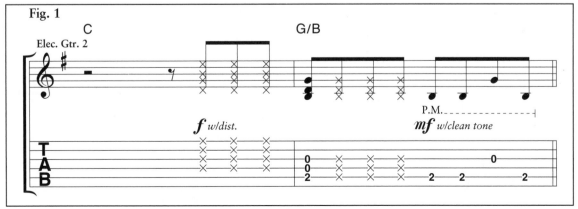

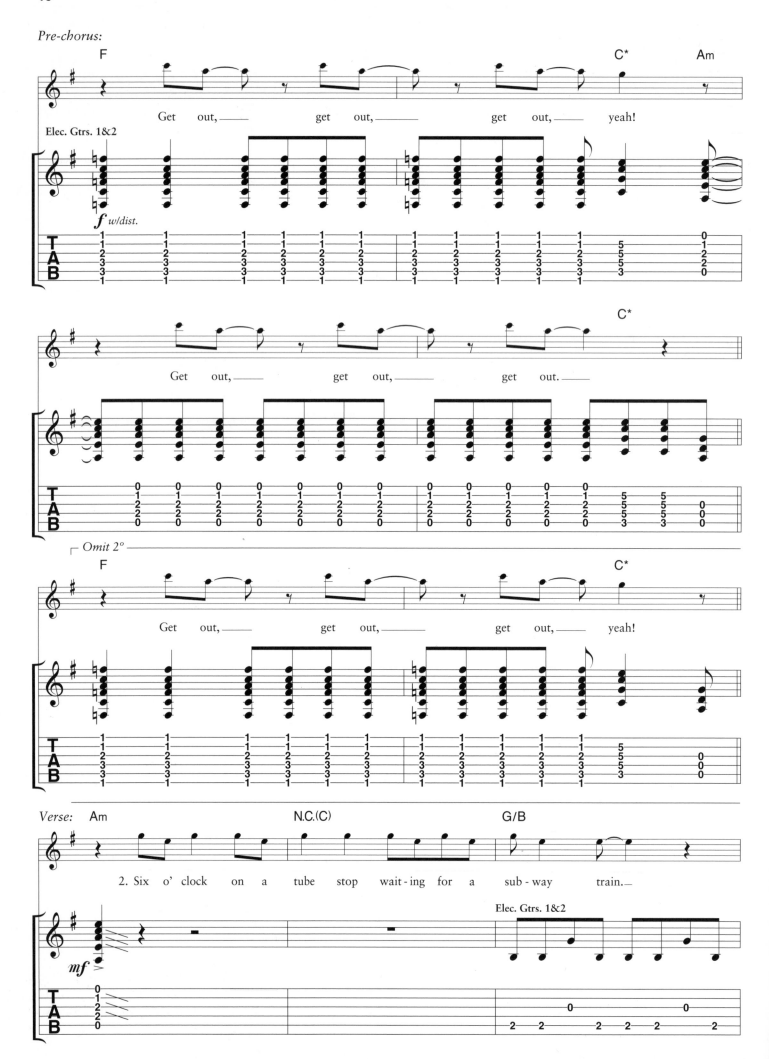

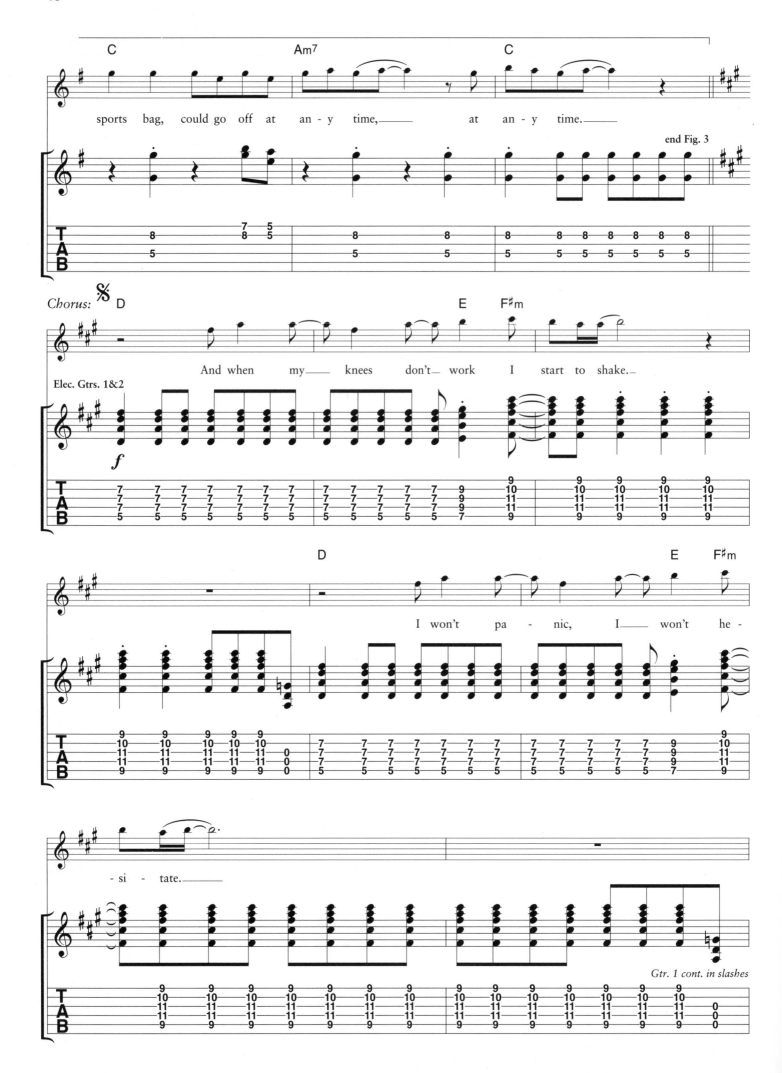

_sports bag, could go off at an - y time,_____ at an - y time._____

end Fig. 3

_Chorus:_

Elec. Gtrs. 1&2

_And when my___ knees don't___ work I start to shake.____

_I won't pa - nic, I___ won't he -_

_- si - tate.____

Gtr. 1 cont. in slashes

# Going Down.

Words and Music by Adam Perry, Giles Perry,
Mark Chapman, Daniel Carter and Jason Perry

© 2001 Warner/Chappell Music Publishing Ltd, London W6 8BS

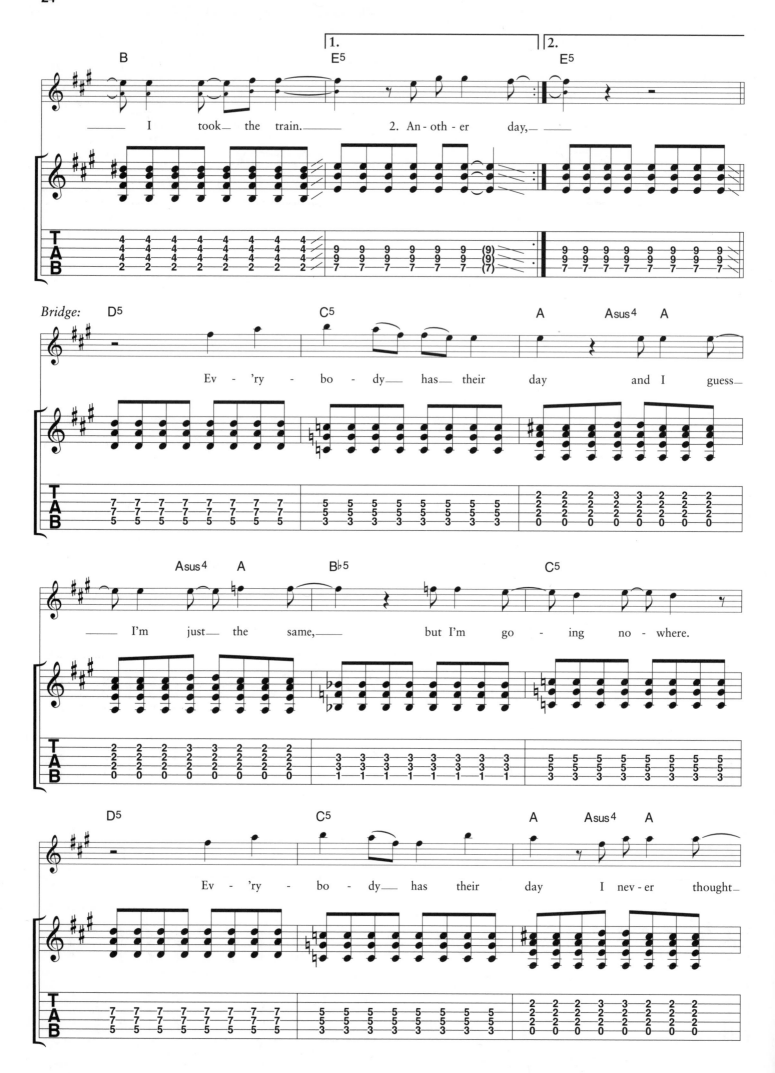

it would be ___ this way, ___ and I real-

-ly don't ___ care. ___

# Took It Away.

Words and Music by Adam Perry, Giles Perry,
Mark Chapman, Daniel Carter and Jason Perry

© 2001 Warner/Chappell Music Publishing Ltd, London W6 8BS

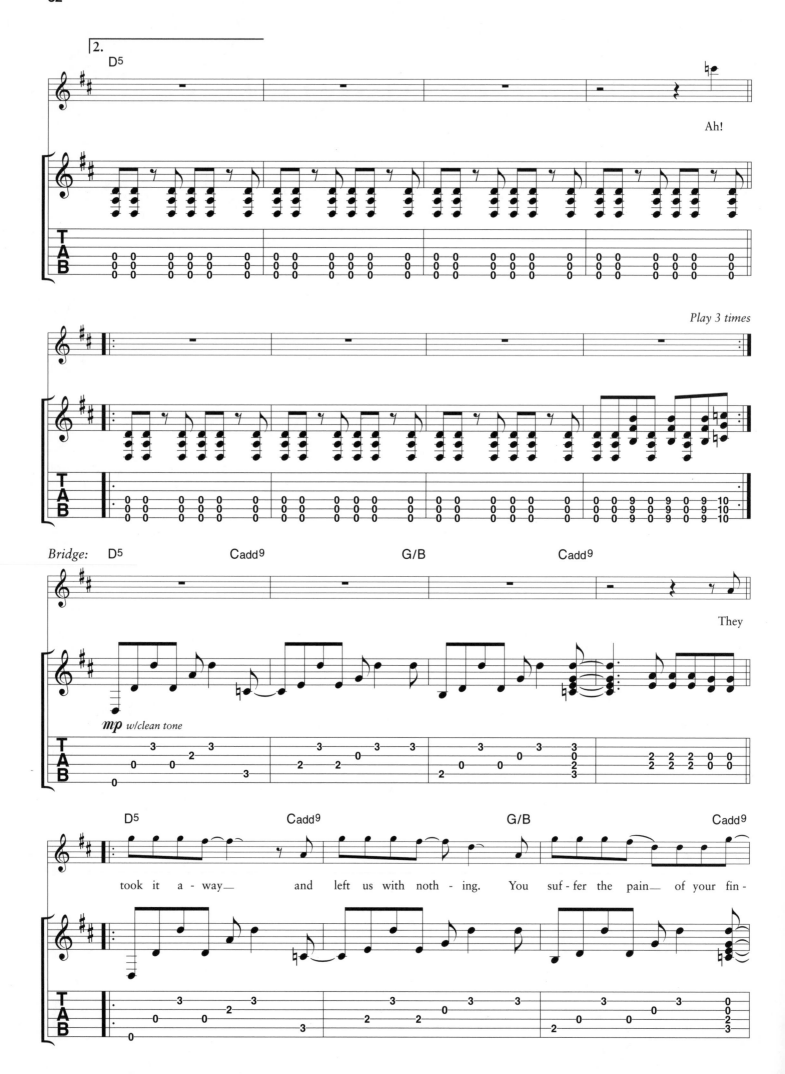

# Starbucks.

Words and Music by Adam Perry, Giles Perry,
Mark Chapman, Daniel Carter and Jason Perry

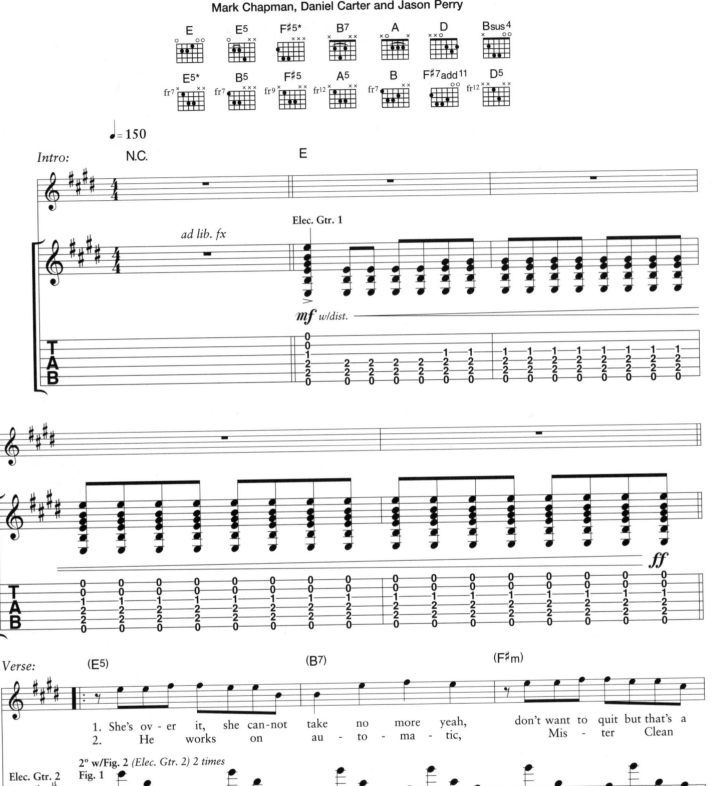

1. She's ov - er it, she can-not take no more yeah, don't want to quit but that's a
2. He works on au - to - ma - tic, Mis - ter Clean

© 2001 Warner/Chappell Music Publishing Ltd, London W6 8BS

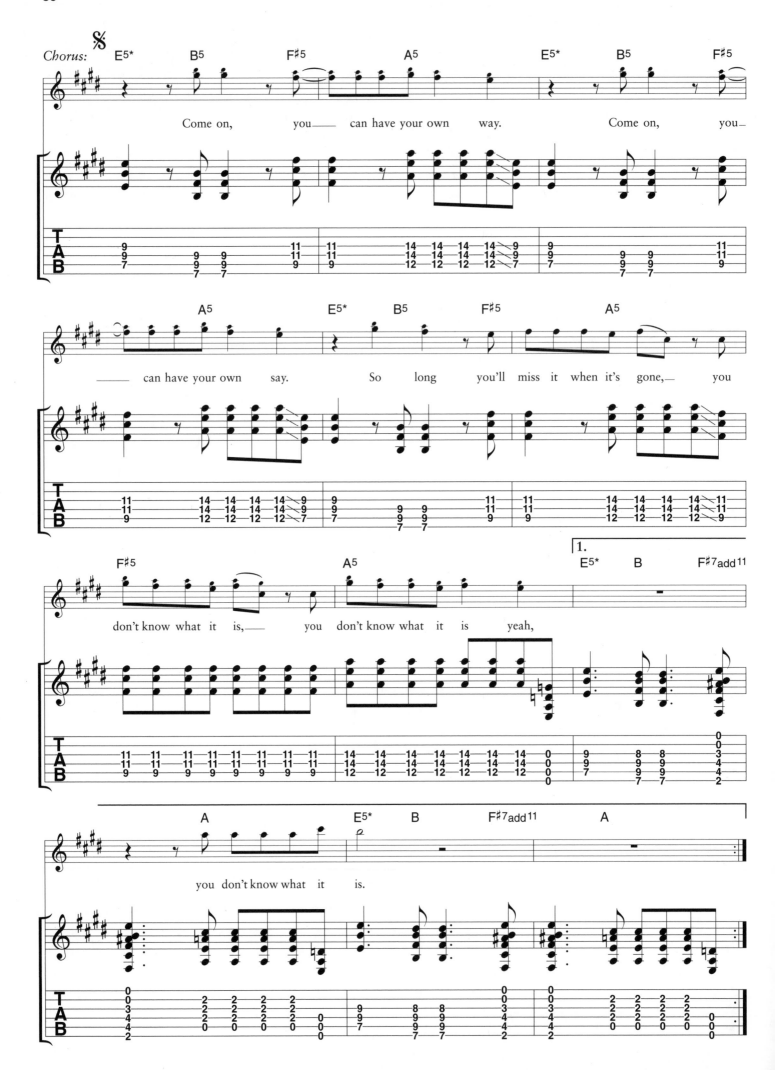

# The Springs.

Words and Music by Adam Perry, Giles Perry,
Mark Chapman, Daniel Carter and Jason Perry

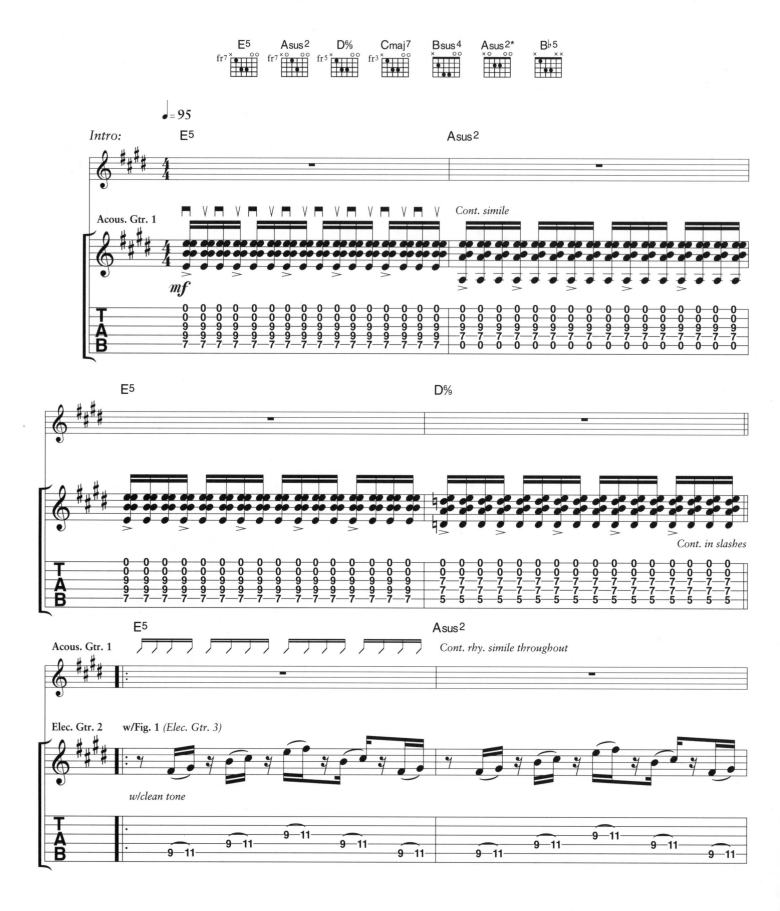

© 2001 Warner/Chappell Music Publishing Ltd, London W6 8BS

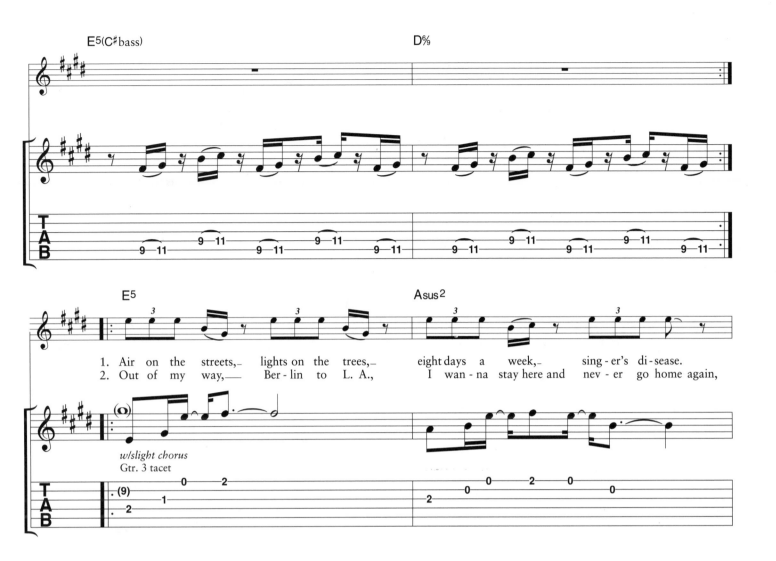

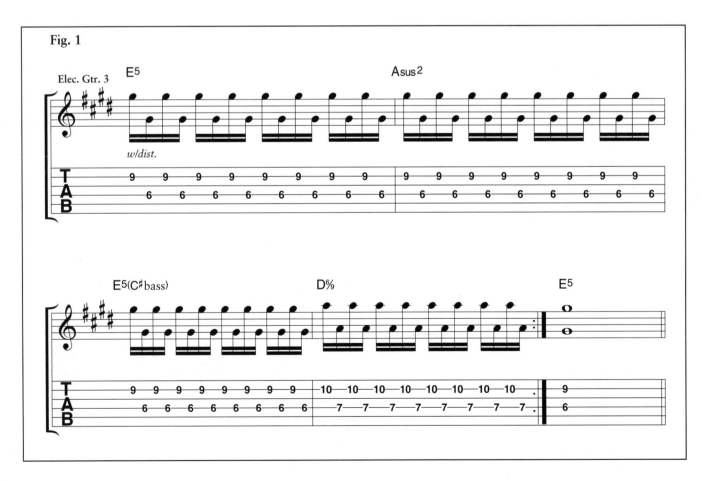

**Fig. 1**

lines. It's a new— day for a new— wave. It's a per-

-fect mo - ment. Oh! I'm mov-ing out— for a mo-ment in— the springs.

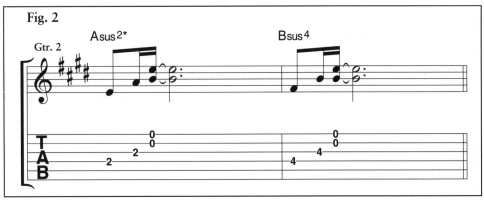

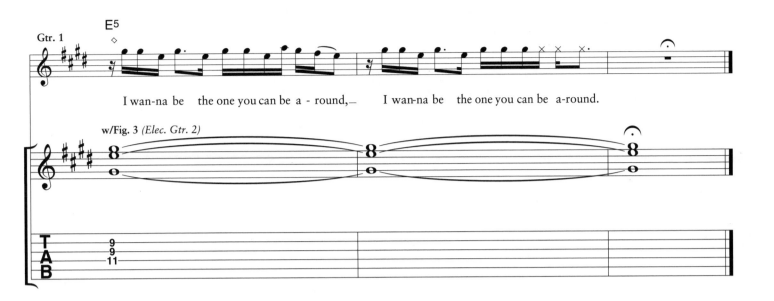

I wan-na be the one you can be a - round,__ I wan-na be the one you can be a-round.

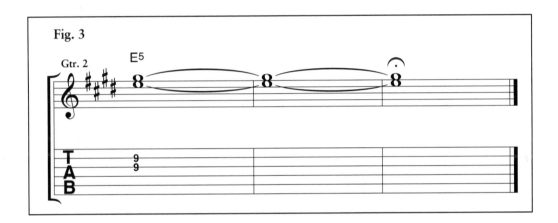

**Fig. 3**

*Verse 3:*
I have to say, your home's where you make it
It's O.K., I know when you fake it
I want to be the gum on your train seat
I want to stand up and walk on my own feet.

*Verse 4:*
I want to be the one you can be around
I want to be the rock underneath your ground
I want to be the one who can make you proud
I want to be the one you can be around.

# Shut Yer Face.

Words and Music by Adam Perry, Giles Perry,
Mark Chapman, Daniel Carter and Jason Perry

© 2001 Warner/Chappell Music Publishing Ltd, London W6 8BS

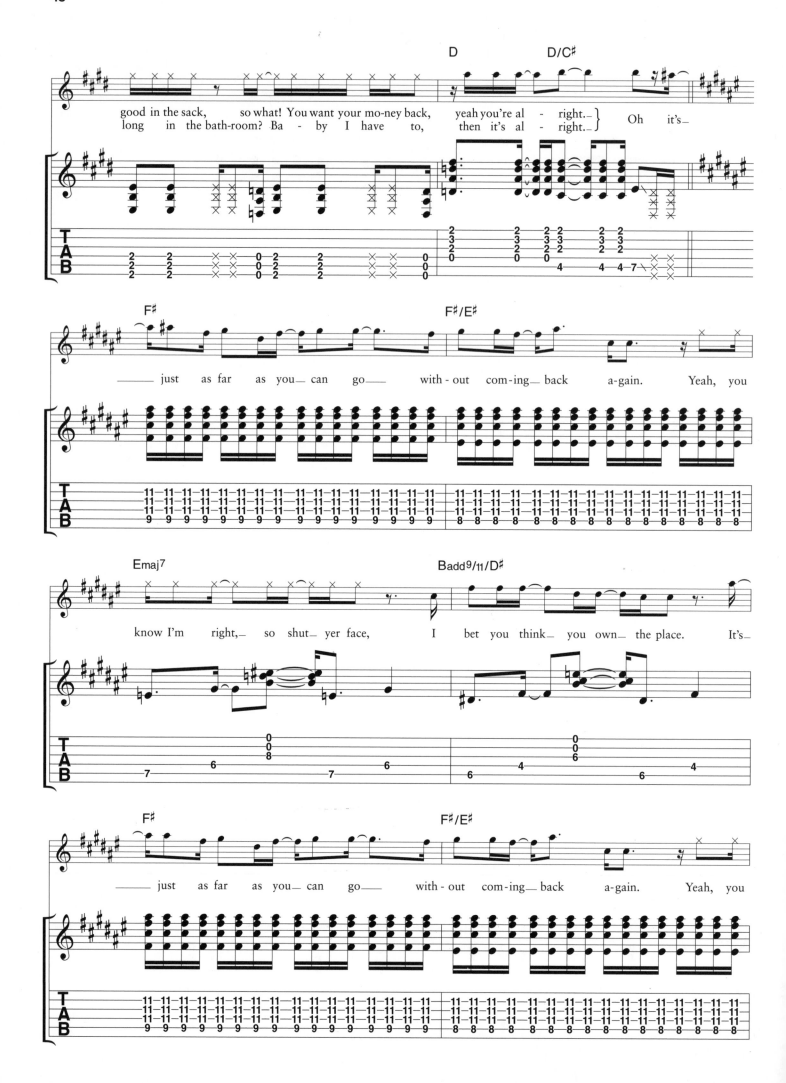

*Recorded with triggered gate fx

*Pre-chorus 3* (𝄌):
Smacking you, whacking you
Flat out attacking you
Beating me down with my words over you
Too hot to handle
Maybe you're mental
But you're alright.

# Pacific Ocean Blue.

Words and Music by Adam Perry, Giles Perry,
Mark Chapman, Daniel Carter and Jason Perry

© 2001 Warner/Chappell Music Publishing Ltd, London W6 8BS

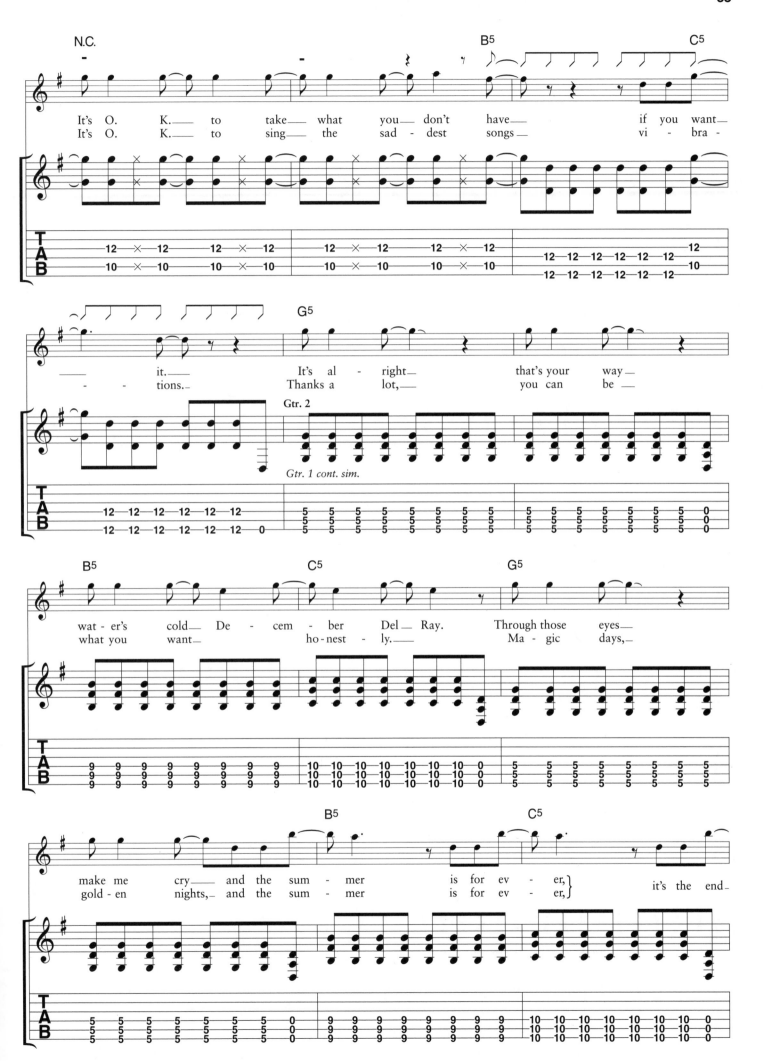

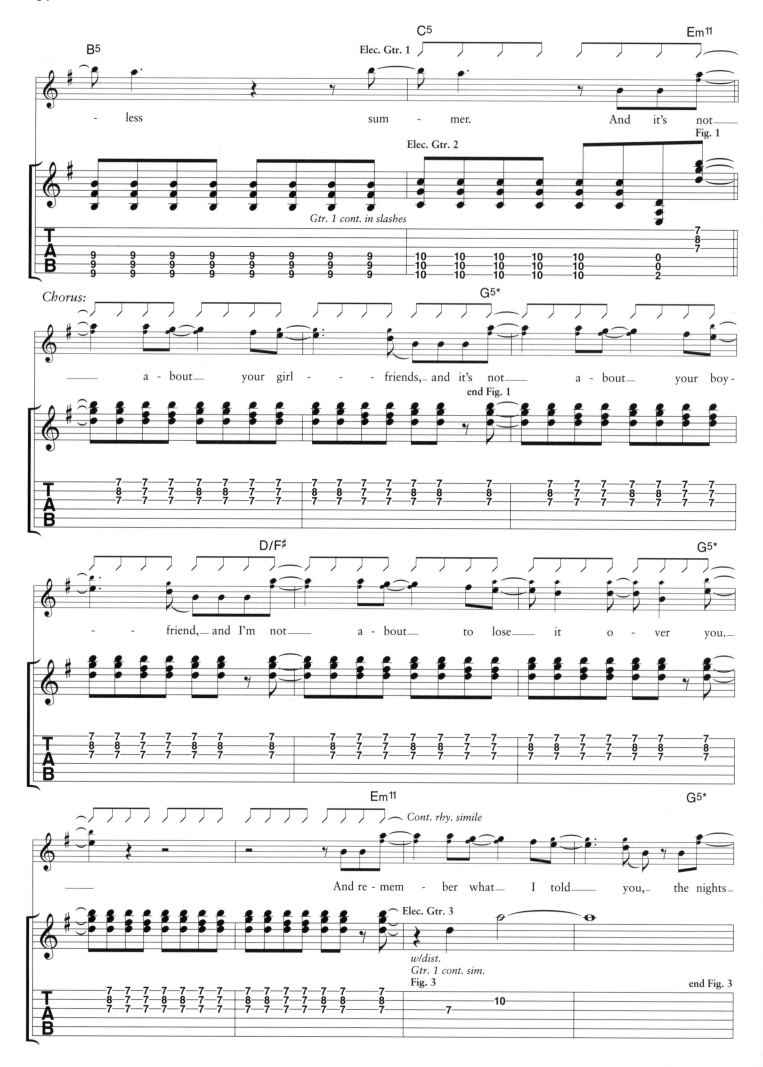

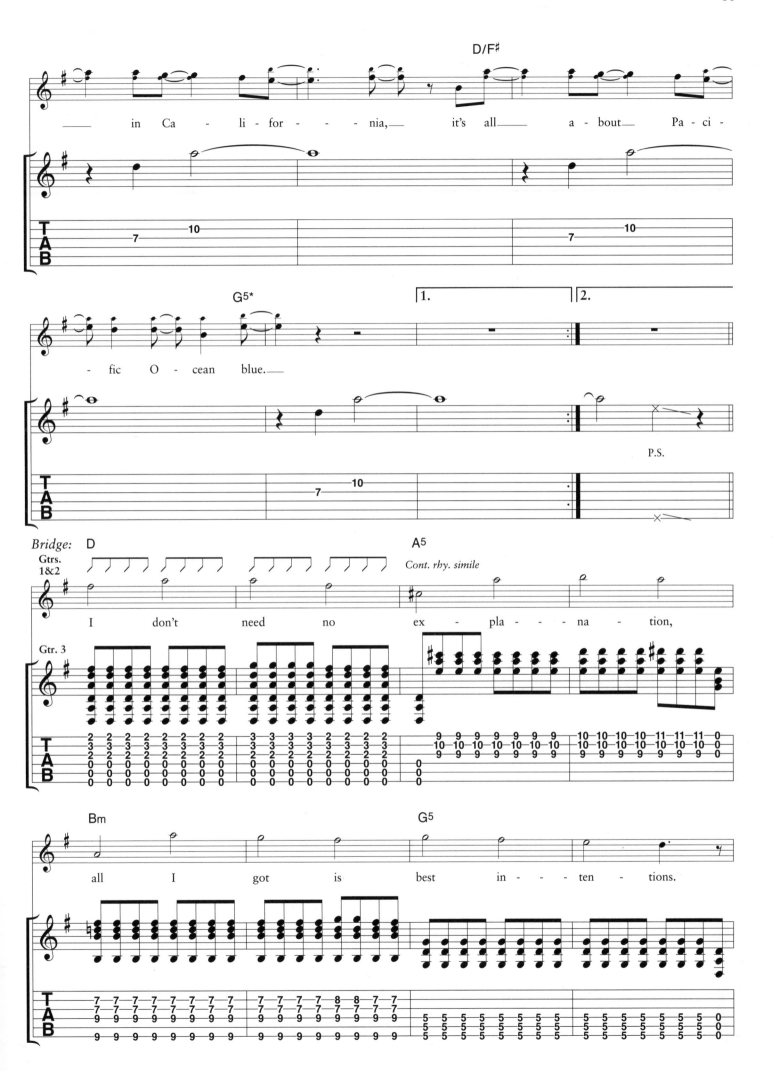

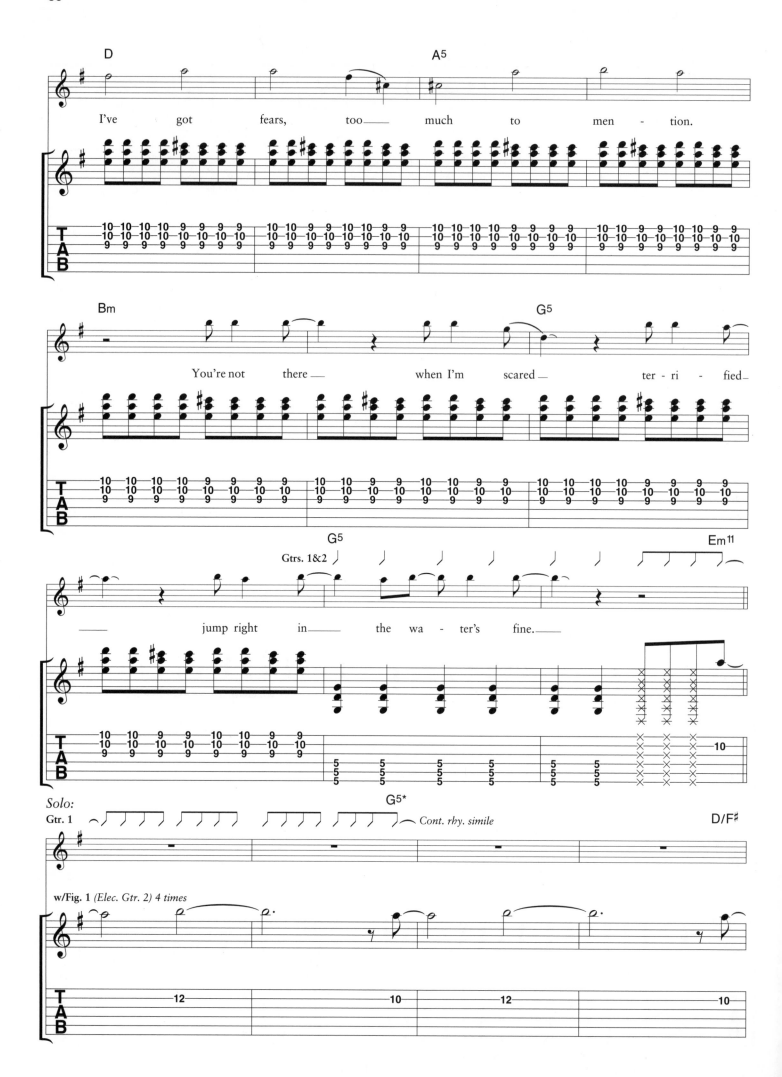

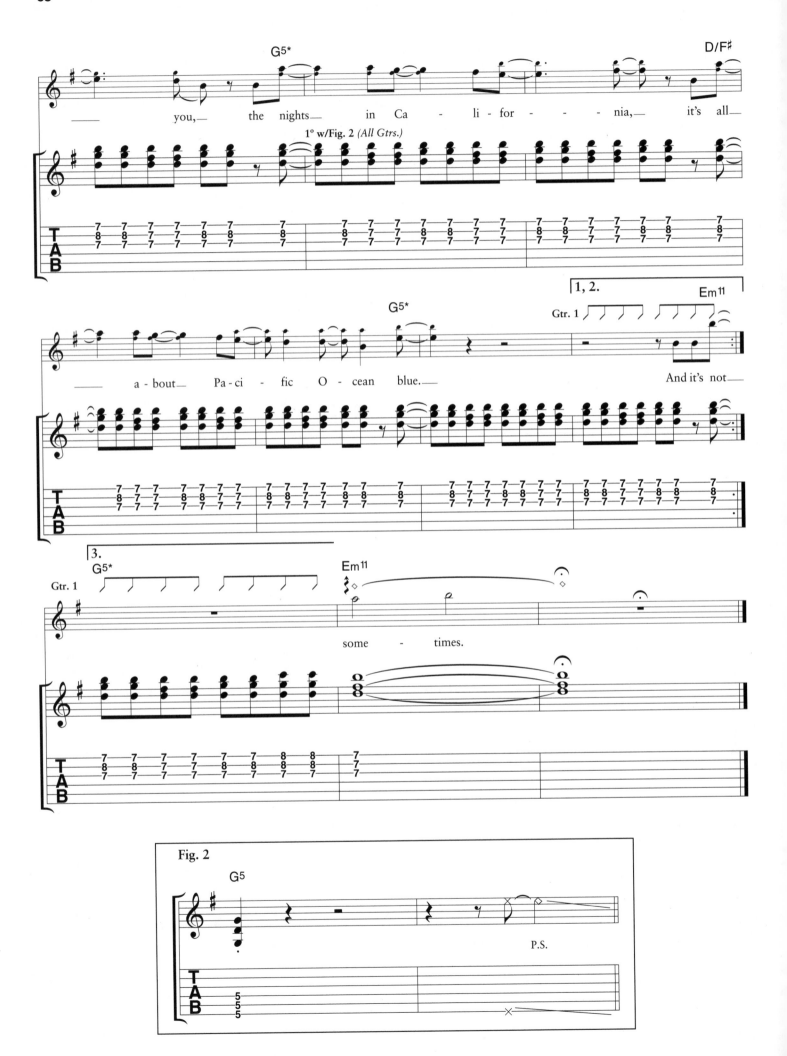

Fig. 2

# The Distance.

Words and Music by Adam Perry, Giles Perry,
Mark Chapman, Daniel Carter and Jason Perry

© 2001 Warner/Chappell Music Publishing Ltd, London W6 8BS

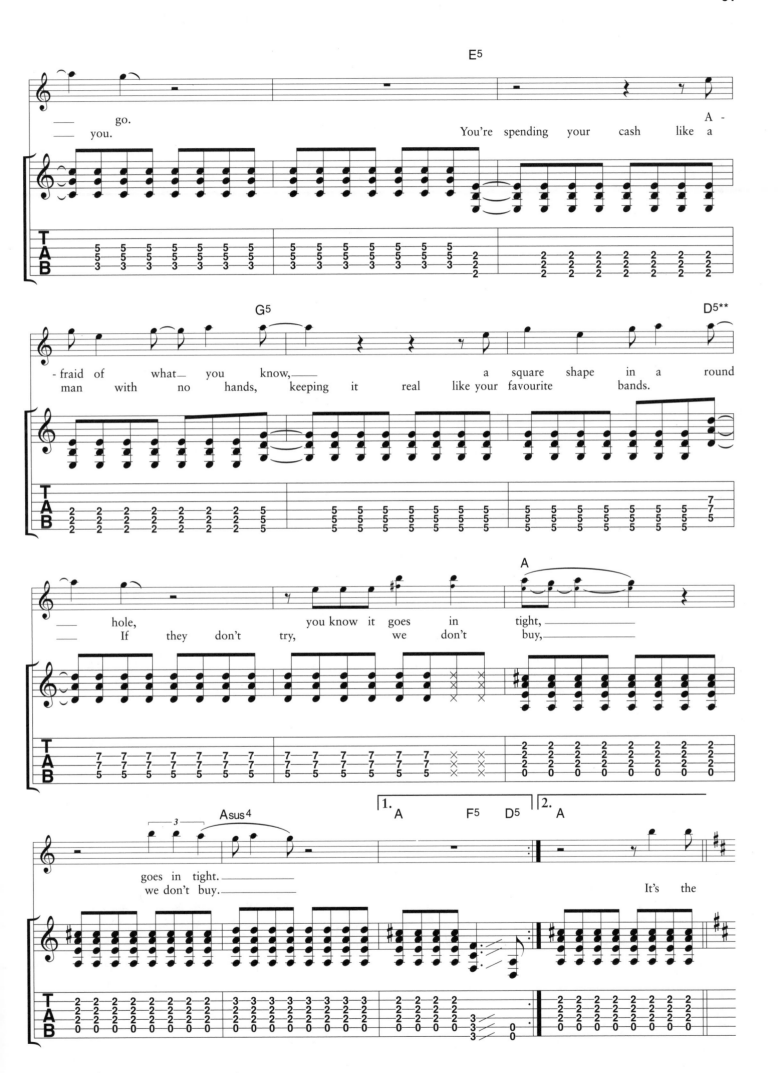

# W.D.Y.C.A.I.

**Words and Music by Adam Perry, Giles Perry,
Mark Chapman, Daniel Carter and Jason Perry**

© 2001 Warner/Chappell Music Publishing Ltd, London W6 8BS

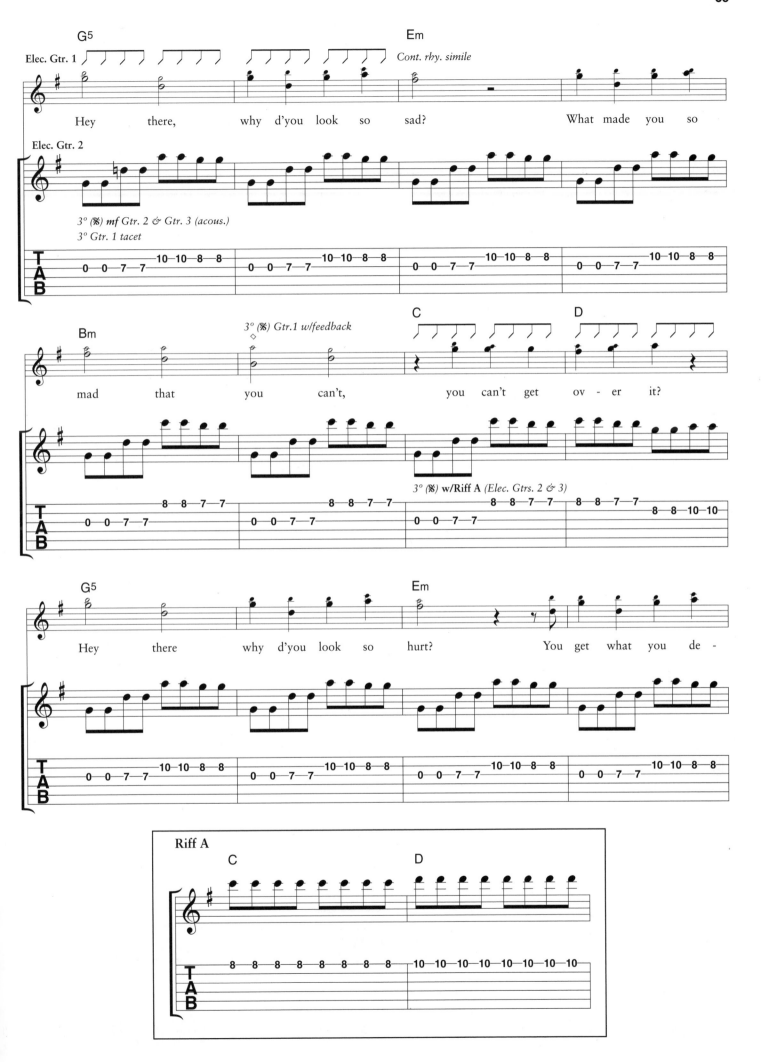

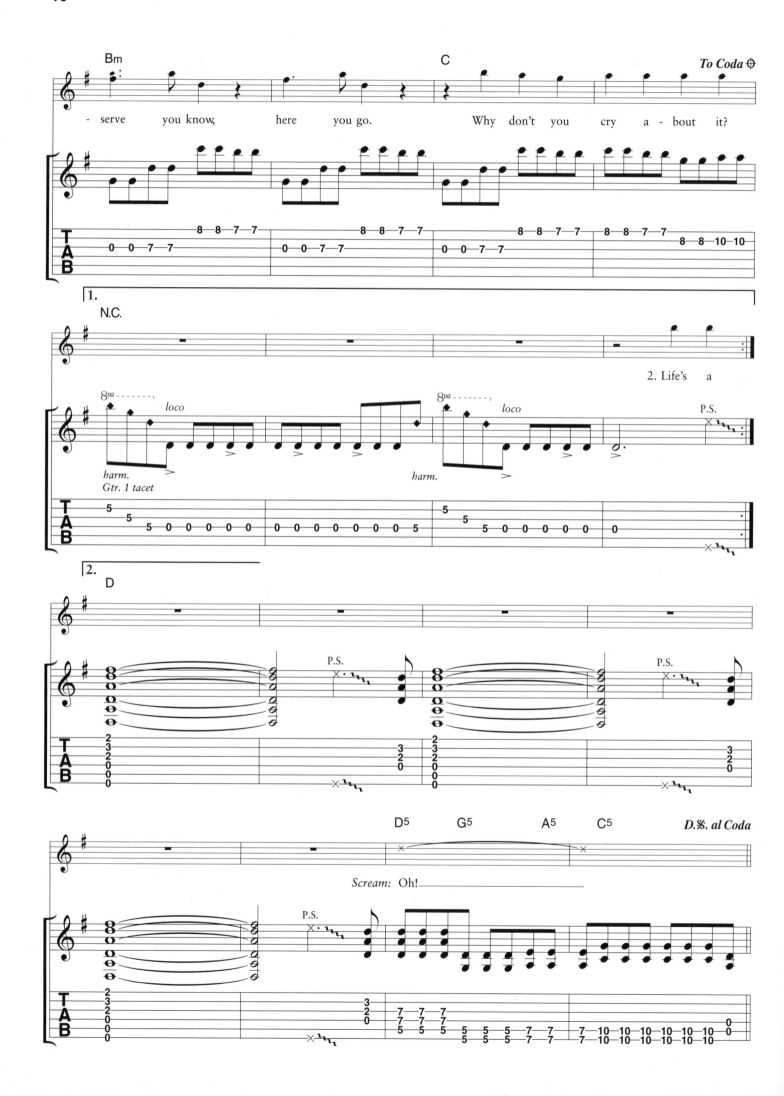

# Hi-Fi Serious.

Words and Music by Adam Perry, Giles Perry,
Mark Chapman, Daniel Carter and Jason Perry

© 2001 Warner/Chappell Music Publishing Ltd, London W6 8BS

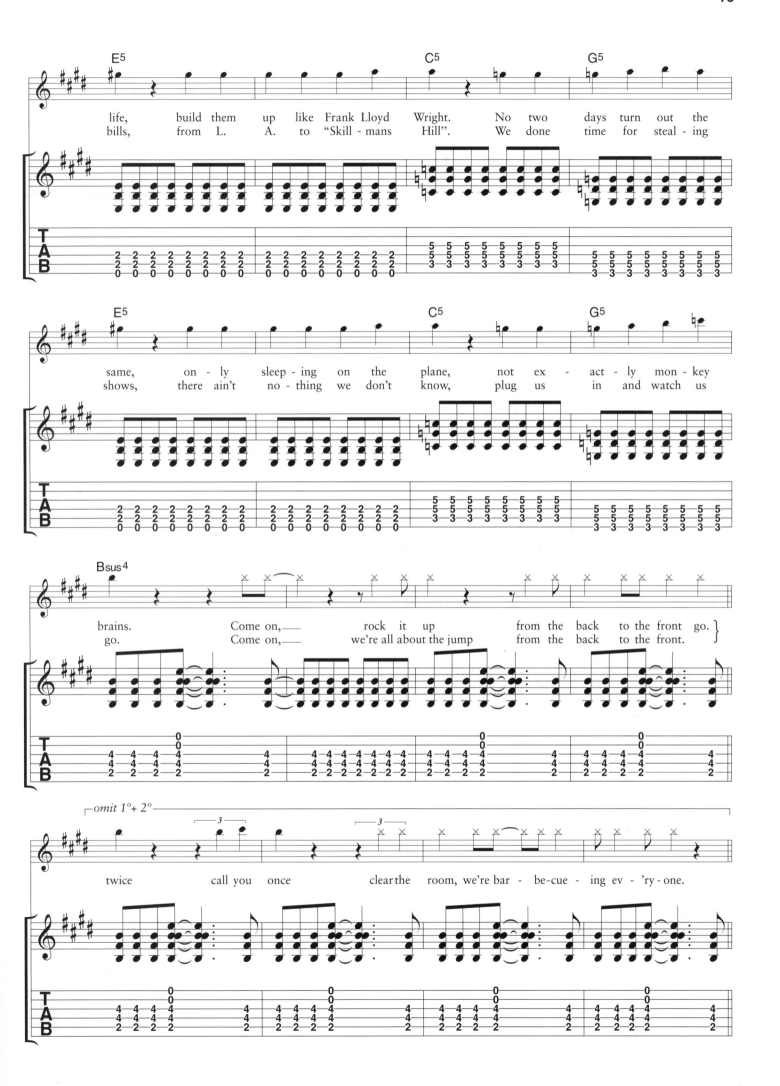

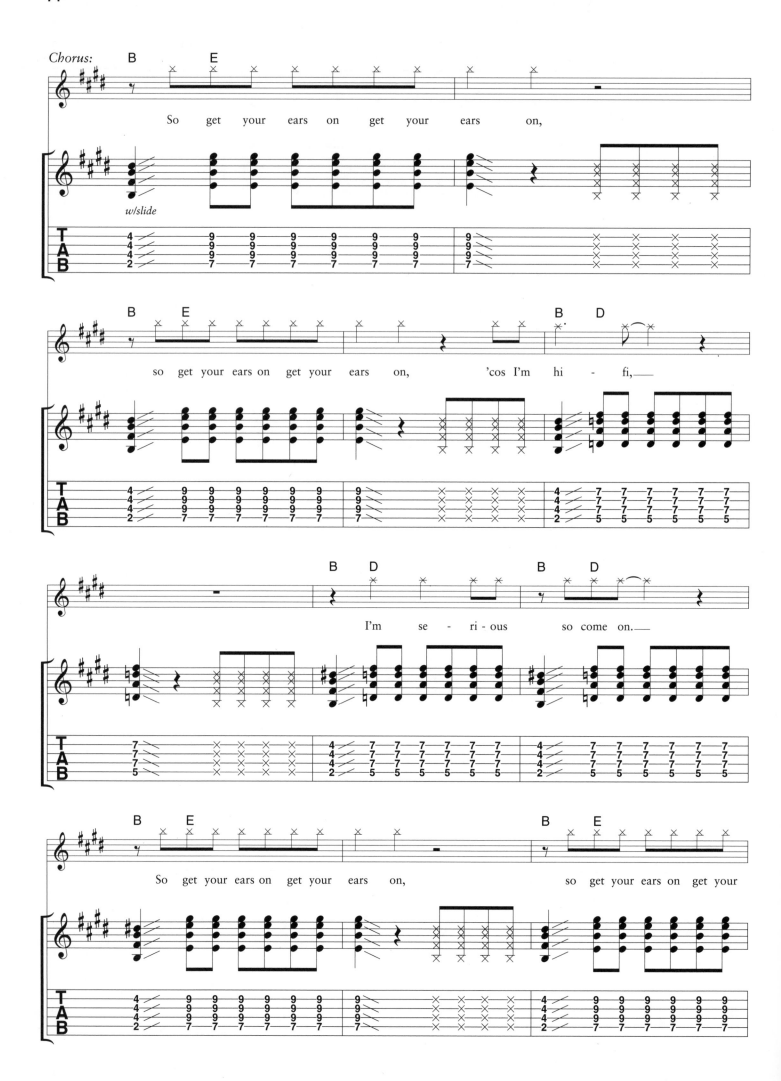

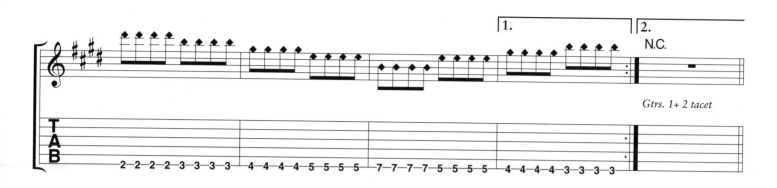

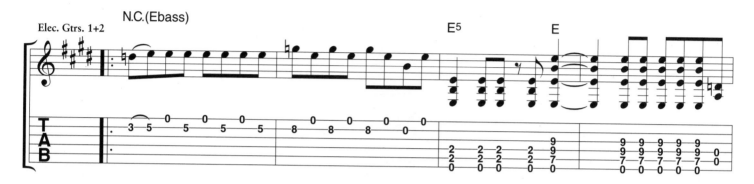

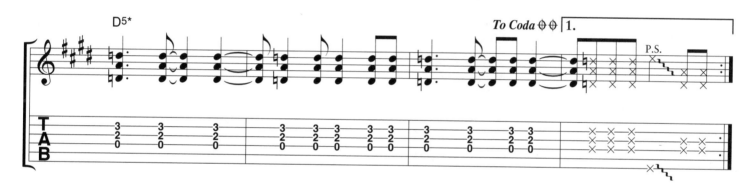

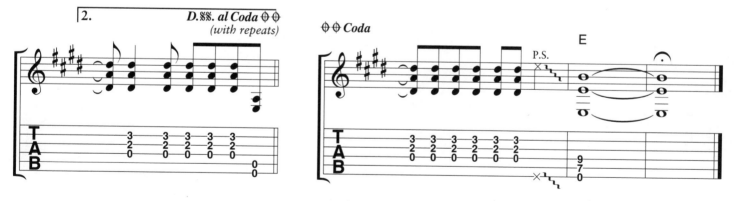

*Verse 3:*
Coming round for one more go
Way too loud for radio
Moshpit full of casualties
OAP's get in for free
Time to even out the score
Thought we'd done enough before
Now we're kicking down your door
Come on! Rock it out!
To the back
Measure twice
Cut it once
Clear the room
We're barbecuing up for lunch.